4 June 1965 -
Vietnam

Paul,
To help you become "integrated" -
into the soul of the country in which
you preside.

Love Ever
Jackie

FOLK TALES FROM VIETNAM

COMPILED BY
GLENN W. MONIGOLD

WITH ILLUSTRATIONS BY
JEANYEE WONG

THE PETER PAUPER PRESS
MOUNT VERNON, NEW YORK

FOLK TALES FROM VIETNAM

THE COUNTRY OF SOUTH VIETNAM

$\mathcal{I}$N ASIA, on the shores of the China Sea, is the little country of South Vietnam. Vietnam was settled by Chinese refugees in search of a new home more than two hundred years ago. Although living in a new land they kept alive the customs they had learned in China. They followed the same religions, Buddhism and Confucianism. One day some French missionaries came to Vietnam and taught the people about Christianity. Today nearly half the Vietnamese are Christians.

Soon after the arrival of the missionaries, France declared that Vietnam, Cambodia and Laos would be protectorates of France and be called French Indo-China. France ruled Indo-China more than eighty years. Then one day the people decided they wanted independence and war broke out. In 1954 the war ended and Vietnam was divided at the seventeenth parallel.

The northern half went to communist rulers and South Vietnam became a democracy.

Vietnam is a long narrow country which has mountains, forests and swamps. In the north central and north regions there are mountains and jungles. There are also many precious minerals and much coal. Living in the jungles and bamboo thickets are many wild animals including tigers and elephants. In the south central and southern parts of Vietnam the land is flat and swampy. Here is where rice is grown. Rice is the main food in Vietnam.

The rainy season in South Vietnam lasts from about July until October. During this period the temperature ranges from about one hundred degrees during the day to as low as sixty-five degrees at night. During the rest of the year the range is from about ninety degrees to one hundred and thirty degrees. Saigon, the capital city and a beautiful place, is only eight degrees above the equator.

THE MOSQUITO STORY

Do you know that only the female mosquitoes bite? Do you know why?

A long time ago Ngoc Tam and his wife Nham Diep lived on a small farm. Tam tended the rice fields and Diep raised silkworms. Diep was a day dreamer. She had visions of one day living in a large house with many servants to wait on her. She hated to work.

One day Diep became ill while Tam was out working in the fields. When Tam got home Diep was dead. As Tam was saying prayers for her a vision came to him. The vision told Tam to take Diep's body by boat to the enchanted mountain in the sea.

After many days of rowing Tam reached the mountain. He carried Diep up the steep path to a lovely field of flowers and laid her down. As he knelt beside her a wrinkled, gray haired old man with sparkling eyes appeared. The old man asked Tam to stay in this place and become a disciple. But Tam said he loved Diep very much and wanted her back. So the old man told Tam to make a small cut on his finger and let three drops of his blood fall on Diep. When this was done Diep awoke to the world of the living again.

The old man told her what had happened. He said she must be faithful, obedient and work very hard or she would be punished. Then the old man was gone and Tam and Diep returned to the boat. On the way home they stopped at a village to buy supplies.

While Diep was waiting for Tam at the dock a large elegant boat came in. The owner, a rich merchant, asked Diep aboard for a cup of tea while his servants repaired the sails. The merchant told Diep she was very beautiful and asked her to sail off with him and become his wife. These were the things Diep had always wanted so she said yes and did not tell the merchant about Tam.

When Tam returned Diep was gone and an old sailor told him what had happened

and where the merchant lived. Tam was very angry. He set out for the merchant's home and in a few days he found it. He told a servant he wanted to see the master and he would wait in the garden. When he got to the garden he came upon Diep cutting some flowers. Diep was very surprised to see Tam here in this place. She said she was happy and would not leave.

Tam said he did not want her back, he only wanted his three drops of blood. Diep was greatly relieved and made a small cut on her finger with the flower knife. Tam held out his arm and Diep let the blood fall on it. When the third drop fell Diep's beauty was gone and she began to shrink until she was the size of a mosquito. That was Diep's punishment! She began buzzing around Tam's head and it sounded as if she was saying, "Give me back the blood, I am sorry, I am sorry."

Tam ran back to his boat and rowed for many days until he found the enchanted mountain again. After he had become a disciple he asked the old man about Diep.

And the old man said that Diep and all the female mosquitoes who came after her would continue to search for the three drops of blood. Then he said, "And this shall be a reminder to all people to live cleanly, be obedient and work honestly." And so it has been ever since.

THE SHADOW AND THE ABSENT

*T*HERE once lived a ruler whose name was Jan-Thi-Hoang. Hoang was a tyrant and imposed heavy taxes on his subjects. The people did not like Hoang and all who spoke out against him were thrown into prison and then sent to help build the great wall of China. Hoang did not like educated people and so he arrested school teachers and scholars and put them to work on the wall too.

One of the school teachers he arrested

was a young man named Chan. Chan and his wife Li lived in the small village where they had grown up together. Their first son was born a month after Chan had been taken away. Li named the boy Chin as this was the name Chan had chosen. Chin was a beautiful baby and Li loved him dearly and felt so grieved that Chan could not see his son. Li felt very sure that Chan would come back to them some day.

When Chin began talking Li taught him from Chan's books. She told him his father was away working but would come back to them soon. Each night when she tucked Chin into bed the two of them would pray for Chan's safe return. When the boy was asleep Li would take the lamp to the window and sit in her rocking chair to wait for Chan. This is the way Li slept each night.

One night, when Chin was about four years old, there was a violent storm. The thunder awoke Chin who cried out. Li placed the lamp on a small table outside Chin's room and as she went through the

door her shadow was cast upon the wall. Chin was frightened when he saw the shadow and asked what it was. "It is the image of your father," Li told him. Chin got on his knees and clasping his hands he bowed down and said, "Good night, dear father." From then on this same ritual was repeated each night at bed time.

One night after Chin was asleep Li was summoned to the temple. As she left the house Chan appeared suddenly and told her he had escaped. Li told him to go in the house and hide and she would be back as soon as she could. She said he should be quiet and not wake Chin. In a few minutes though Chin awoke and cried out. Chan went to the door and said, "Be not afraid son, it is I, your father." In a sobbing voice Chin said, "Go away, you are not my father. My father is away and comes to me each night when I go to bed." Then he lay down and went back to sleep.

Chan did not know what to think. Li had hurried off without telling him where she was going and now his own son told

14

him of a strange man putting him to bed at night. Chin was afraid Li had lost her love for him and had possibly remarried. As he thought about it he became angry and decided to leave. When Li returned she said, "Some soldiers are in town, my lord, and you are in danger!" Li could see that Chan was angry and asked him why. Chan told her his suspicions and then ran out the door.

Li realized how unhappy Chan must be, and she was very sad. She searched for Chan but could find no trace of him and in her great sorrow she threw herself off the high cliff into the river below. The neighbors took little Chin in to live with them.

The next day it was decreed that all the school teachers were pardoned and could return to their homes. Chan heard the news at the place he was hiding and left at once for his village. When he arrived he heard the terrible story of Li and went to the neighbors for Chin. It was dark when they got home and it was Chin's bed time. When Chin was ready for bed he called to his father. Chan placed the lamp on the table by Chin's room and as he walked through the door his shadow was cast upon the wall. Chin got on his knees, clasped his hands and bowed down to the shadow saying, "Good night, dear mother." And so Chan discovered the whole truth.

Chan built an altar on the high cliff and each evening he and Chin go there to worship the memory of a loving wife and mother.

THE DA TRANG STORY

$\mathcal{E}$ACH morning, at dawn, Da Trang the hunter left his little house and went into the forest with his bow and arrows. He came back at twilight with the game he had shot. Each day Da Trang walked through the ruins of an ancient temple where two spotted snakes lived. The first time he saw them he was frightened but as

the snakes paid no attention to him he soon lost his fear. After a while he even gave the snakes some food each day on his way home from the hunt.

One day, as he neared the old temple, Da Trang heard some noise in the brush. He ran to the place and saw a large yellow snake attacking his two friendly snakes. He shot an arrow at the big snake and it ran off with one of the spotted ones chasing it. The other snake was dead so Da Trang dug a grave and buried it.

That night Da Trang was awakened by a gentle voice calling his name. He sat up in his bed and saw the spotted snake standing beside him. Then the snake spoke, "Do not be alarmed, I am your friend. I wish to reward you for the great deed you performed today." Then the snake placed something in Da Trang's hand and was gone. Da Trang held the object up and saw a bright shiny pearl. Now it has been said that the owner of a snake genius pearl could talk with any living animal by holding the pearl in his mouth.

The next morning Da Trang put the pearl in his mouth and went into the woods. He came upon a crow sitting high up in a tree and asked it if it saw any game around. The crow said there was a deer about two hundred feet to the right. Da Trang shot the deer and gave the crow a generous portion. From then on the two worked together.

One day the crow was late coming for his food and a wolf ate it. The crow was very angry and accused Da Trang of not leaving the food. They argued very loudly and Da Trang shot an arrow at the crow who caught it in his claws and swore vengeance. The next day another hunter was found dead with Da Trang's arrow through his heart.

Da Trang was arrested and put in prison. He wasn't lonely because he could talk with all the birds, insects and rodents. And he heard many tales from his quaint friends. When he heard the sparrows bragging about stealing from the king's granary he reported it to the jailer. The jailer asked the granary keeper if he had been losing grain and the keeper said yes but didn't know where it had been going. When Da Trang saw the ants moving he asked them why and they said the river was going to flood. Da Trang told the jailer who went to warn the king. The king just laughed at the story, but when the river began to rise and the whole countryside was flooded the king realized his mistake. He sent for Da Trang.

When the king learned Da Trang's secret he made Da Trang his personal minister and the two men went every place together. Da Trang would tell the king what the animals were saying and this pleased the king very much. One day they were out in the king's boat and Da Trang was standing by the rail talking to some fish. One of the fish began reciting a silly poem which amused Da Trang and he laughed and laughed. As he did so the pearl slipped from his mouth and sank out of sight. Da Trang began sobbing and told the king what had happened, but the king said, "Do not worry, I shall send divers to recover the pearl."

The divers searched for many days but could not find the pearl. Da Trang was heart-broken and asked the king if he could still keep on looking. "Yes," said the king. Da Trang decided he would fill the sea with sand as far out as the place he had lost his pearl. Thereupon, the king gave Da Trang a large crew of men and the job began. They worked and worked but the sea grew no smaller. As each load of sand was thrown into the water the next wave would wash it away. Then all the workmen were taken away and Da Trang was left alone. He worked day and night until he died. He was buried on a little hill overlooking the place he had lost his pearl.

Now when we go to the beach we see hordes of tiny Da Trang crabs busily working in the sand. We see them make little mounds of sand and then the next wave washes the mounds away. But they do not give up. It is said that the soul of Da Trang, still looking for the pearl, lives in these tiny crabs. It is also said the Da Trang crabs are to remind us to use common sense and moderation in each thing we do.

THE LOVE CRYSTAL

MANY years ago Nuhn Li Te was the ruler of a small Province in Vietnam. Te lived in a castle on the banks of a river with his wife An and daughter Nam.

When Nam was a little girl she played in all parts of the castle but her favorite place was a room in the tower. Here she could see the river for many miles and she loved to watch the boats sailing up and down the river. When Nam was old enough to choose her own room she decided on the high tower room. She would sit all day by the window and read or embroider, — that is when she wasn't watching the river.

One morning Nam heard beautiful sing-ing from the river and when she looked down she saw a small boat with a young fisherman in it. Nam was very excited and knew she was in love with this wonderful singer. She could not see his face but with a voice like that he just had to be hand-some! Each morning after that Nam was at the window waiting for her singing fisherman.

One morning Nam waited and waited but the little boat with the singing fisher-man did not come. A week went by and still no boat! Nam became ill and refused to talk or eat. She just sat by the window day and night watching and waiting. Her maid was very sorry to see Nam like this and so she went to Nam's father and told him the story.

Nuhn Li Te sent his servants out to search for the fisherman and they found him in the next village. His name was Tan. The ruler told Tan all about Nam and then took him to the room at the top of the tower. When they entered the room Tan

began singing and Nam became flushed and excited. Her father said, "Nam, this is Tan the fisherman, this is the young man you love." Nam sat staring at Tan and as he walked towards her the expression on her face changed to show fright and discontentment. Tan was not handsome. Covering her face with her hands she cried out, "No, no, I do not love him, take him away!"

Tan returned to his village and was very sad. In that brief moment he had seen Nam's great beauty, and he had fallen in love with her. In a short time Tan died of a broken heart, and Tan's body was placed in a casket for burial late one evening. In the morning when his family returned they found a small gem resembling a crystal lying on top. They took the gem to the ruler, Nuhn Li Te, who told them it was a love crystal. He ordered a cup of tea and dropped the crystal in it. In the cup there appeared an image of a fisherman rowing a small boat around and around. Then the ruler uttered these words,

"No tinh chua tra cho ai, Khoi Tinh mang ocuong tuyen dai chua tan."

In Vietnamese these words mean, "The gem of love won't dissolve after death so long as the debt of love remains."

In Vietnam it is believed that the love of every young couple has been pre-determined in another life. When two people fall in love they shall remain together in life and after death.

When Nam saw the vision in the tea she knew what she had done. She had taken Tan's love but had not returned it, and she knew what she must do!

She took the cup of tea to her room in the tower where she was all alone. She sat in her chair and held the cup in her lap. Then she began sobbing and the tears fell into the cup. The crystal began to melt and when it was all dissolved Nam sat very still and lifeless. Nam and Tan were together in another world.

THE MOUNT OF WAITING

NEAR Lang-Son, in North Vietnam, on a cliff high above the sea, there is a strange rock formation. The rock looks like a woman standing there, holding a baby in her arms, searching out to sea. Sailors call the cliff, "The Mount of Waiting," and they say the rock was a woman who turned to stone.

Many years ago, near the village of Lang-Son, there lived a farmer and his wife who had a son and daughter. The parents were killed during a violent storm when the son, Lan, was fourteen and the daughter, Nam, was only nine years old. Lan and Nam were a loving brother and sister and so they stayed together and ran the farm.

One day a circus came to Lang-Son and Lan and Nam went to see it. There was a fortune-teller with the circus so Lan had his fortune told. The wise man told Lan that because of the great love he and Nam had for each other that one day they would become man and wife. Lan did not want to believe what he heard but he knew this man was very wise and spoke only the truth. Lan also knew this thing must not happen so he would have to prevent it. He did not tell Nam what the prophet had said.

The next Sunday Lan and Nam went into the forest to cut and gather wood for their fires. As Nam was preparing a lunch for them Lan sneaked up behind her and struck her on the head with his axe. Then he turned and ran from the place as fast as he could. Lan traveled for many days until he came to a village many miles from Lang-Son. He changed his name to Tan and apprenticed himself to a merchant.

Tan worked very hard and soon learned the trade. When the merchant retired he put Tan in charge and when he died he left the business to Tan in his will. One day a farmer and his wife and daughter came into the store. They were Mr. and Mrs. Win and their daughter's name was San and they had just come from a far-away place.

San was very beautiful and Tan fell in love with her. In a short while they were married and in a year they had a son.

Now that Tan had a family he did not go on many buying trips, but sent one of his workmen in his stead. One night San was combing her lovely hair when Tan took the comb from her and began doing it for her. On the back of San's head Tan saw a large scar and asked her how she got it, and as she told him her story, Tan suddenly realized who she was. She said some hunters had found her in the woods and had taken her to the Wins' who kept her as their own daughter. At first she could remember nothing of what had happened and then when her memory came back she kept the secret to herself. Tan was the first person she had told about it.

Tan was quite ill and knew now that the prophet's words had been true. He couldn't tell San the truth so he told her he had to leave at once on a buying trip and would be back soon. Tan was gone a week, a month, and then six months. San asked all travelers coming through the village if they had seen Tan, and she sent servants to search for him but there was no trace of her husband. By this time San had realized who Tan was.

Taking her baby, San returned to Lang-Son and her old farm home. Every day San and the baby went to the cliff and looked out to sea for her husband's boat. She was certain he would return to Lang-Son. There she stood, waiting and watching, forgetting about all things else, until she turned to stone!

THE NOSEY NEIGHBOR

WHEN Anh was a little girl she lived in a small village where her father was a blacksmith. Anh had three sisters and four brothers. They were a very happy family. The children all went to school and during their holidays, they played games, went swimming and had lots of fun with all the other village children. Anh was the oldest girl and helped her mother a great deal with the house work.

In the house next door there lived a widow lady whose name was Mrs. Ex. No one in town liked Mrs. Ex very well, and when the children played outdoors, Mrs. Ex would scold them for being so noisy. When a ball rolled into her yard the children had to get it with a long stick so they wouldn't tread on her grass. Sometimes Mrs. Ex would tell the children they were playing a game wrong and give them new rules to follow.

Mrs. Ex didn't annoy only children! She tried to advise adults too. If she heard her neighbors having an argument she would go right into their house and try to settle it. Then she would tell everyone she met that day what the argument was about and how she had settled it. People called her the town gossip.

Mrs. Ex used to spend a lot of time at Anh's house telling Anh's mother all the

gossip and giving advice. Mrs. Ex would tell Anh's mother how to cook and bake or how to sew a better seam. Anh's mother was always very polite to Mrs. Ex; she served her tea and cake and thanked her for her wonderful advice.

One day after Mrs. Ex had left Anh asked her mother why she listened to the woman and why she treated her so kindly. Anh said that no one else in town liked the woman, — everyone said she was a busy-body, a gossip, and was always sticking her nose into other people's business. Anh's mother smiled and answered, "Every one has faults and weak points, no one is perfect. The people who talk that way about Mrs. Ex are equally bad! Mrs. Ex is very outspoken, and likes to criticize, but underneath it all she is a very considerate person. She wants to be helpful in the only way she knows. We must not judge people too quickly or too harshly. We must not see only their bad points."

When Mrs. Ex died and her will was read the townspeople were greatly surprised. Mrs. Ex had left a large sum of money which had been donated to many good causes. There was to be a new play-field for the children, new equipment for the hospital and a new school building. In her will, she said she had been aware of the ill feelings against her by all the villagers save one. This person had been her dearest friend, to whom she left all her blessings. This person was Anh's mother!

Anh never forgot Mrs. Ex nor her mother's words of wisdom.

THE SILVER RIVER

On a clear night, when we look up in the sky, we see a large white band which looks like a fine silk scarf. This is the Silver River.

Chuc Nu was the most beautiful woman in the Heavenly Empire. Chuc Nu was the Divine Spinner and each morning took her spinning wheel to the banks of the Silver River where she worked to the rhythm of the silver waves. Ngau Lang was the Divine Shepherd and each day watched over his flock feeding on the green grass by the banks of the Silver River.

One day Lang came upon Nu spinning and he stopped to talk to her, and, of course, the beautiful young girl and the handsome young man fell in love. In a few days the sheep had eaten all the grass so Nu agreed to work somewhere else if Lang would move her spinning wheel. From then on they worked together and while Nu spun her fine cloth Lang told her wonderful tales.

After a while the young couple went to the Heavenly Emperor and asked his permission to marry. He gave them his blessings but told them they must continue to do their jobs. But the young people, so happy with their new life, soon forgot the warning. They picked flowers, climbed the hills and went swimming. Lang lost some of his sheep and Nu was spinning very little yarn.

The Heavenly Emperor summoned them before him and scolded them for disobeying him. He said they must be punished, and so he separated them. Lang would tend his flocks on one side of the Silver River and Nu would spin on the other side. They would be separated eleven months each year, and at the start of the twelfth month a bridge of ravens would be formed across the river and they could be together for that month.

The two young people separated without a word, and without looking at one another. They were both very sad. When Lang and Nu got to the places they were to occupy they both fell to the ground and began sobbing. Then their sobs turned to bitter tears and they cried until their tears were gone. But as they cried the rain fell in Vietnam; and the rain continued until Lang and Nu stopped crying. Each year after Lang and Nu are separated they cry until their tears are gone, and that is why the rainy season comes to Vietnam each year at the same time.

After the Heavenly Father had punished Lang and Nu he issued a proclamation which told of the punishment and which said,

> *"And each year all the ravens (crows) of Vietnam shall fly to the Heavenly Empire and form a bridge. And henceforth the Silver River shall be seen by all people on earth to remind them to obey the laws of God, and the laws of man. And all people shall respect their parents."*

We can still see the Silver River but today we call it the Milky Way!

THE CARABAO

𝓘N VIETNAM the carabao, or water buffalo, is used as a work animal in the rice paddies. The carabao looks very much like a cow with a hump on its back. Its color is a dark bluish-gray and its large flat horns curve backwards along its neck. It loves to

wallow in the mud. A heavy wooden yoke, with a plow attached, is placed over the necks of two carabao and they pull the plow through the water and mud with the greatest of ease.

Many many years ago the carabao were wild animals living in the forests. They were lazy and shiftless, and they used paths made by other animals. They stole the grass that other animals found and drank all the water. But they only *drank* the water; they never bathed in it! They hated to get wet and during the rainy season they sought shelter from the rain and stayed out of the mud. But even though they were unclean and had a terrible odor the carabao were beautiful! Their horns were long and sharp, their bodies smooth and muscular.

The other animals stayed away from the carabao, partly because of their brute strength and partly because of their offensive odor. But one day when the animals were having one of their monthly meetings someone made a complaint against the carabao. The elephant, who was chairman, trumpeted for order and when all was quiet he said, "Perhaps it is time we do something about those creatures. Are there any suggestions?" There were numerous ideas and opinions voiced but the deer seemed to have the best plan. He said, "Let us appoint one of our stronger members, Mr. Tiger, as our representative. Let the tiger take a message to the carabao. Tell them to start bathing, to stop eating our food and drinking our water and to help us with some of the work. If they refuse we will drive them from our homeland."

So the tiger left to look for the carabao. When he found them he climbed a tree and called out to them, "Oh carabao, can you hear me?" The carabao were surprised and they raised their heads and looked around. Then a great bull spoke out, "Yes, we hear you. Who are you and what do you want?" From his vantage point in the tree the tiger answered, "I come from a meeting of the other animals with this message. We want you to work with us, to help us gather grass, and to start bathing. You are a disgrace to the animal kingdom." Without hesitating the great bull said, "Begone with you! Go tell your friends if they do not like it here to go elsewhere. We are not common animals, we are mighty beasts. No one tells us what to do. If you or your friends bother us again we shall destroy you all."

The tiger returned to the meeting and gave his report. The committee of animals got terribly excited and all began talking at once. Once again the elephant sounded his trumpet for order. Then he said, "Friends, we shall ask the Divine One for guidance. Let us pray." And when the prayers were finished there was a great silence. And then from nowhere came a gentle voice, which said, "Animals, you are right. Too long has the carabao lived in disgrace. He has made no effort to change his ways. He must be punished. All the tigers will go now and attack the carabao herd."

So all the tigers set out on their mission and when they saw the herd they began their carefully planned attack. And when the battle was over no tiger had been hurt but the carabao were a sorry looking sight. Their beautiful horns had been flattened and bent backwards and they had many wounds. The carabao that had not died managed to stumble to a stream where they lay in the shallow water and healed their wounds. In a few days they felt better. When they had regained their strength the carabao had a meeting to decide what to do. The older and wiser ones thought it best to move out of the area but the young ones wanted to stay and to fight the other animals. While they were arguing and bickering a strange voice came to them. It was the same voice that had spoken to the other animals. The voice said, "Carabao, you have been punished for your miserable ways. But this is only part of the punishment. From this time on you shall be a beast of burden to punish you for your laziness. You shall be ugly because you boasted of your beauty, and you shall enjoy wallowing about in mud and water because of your uncleanliness. Go now towards the nearest village and give yourselves to the farmers living there. You will pull their plows through the muddy rice fields forever."

And so the water buffalo or carabao have had humped shoulders, flat useless horns. And they have been wallowing about in mud and pulling plows in rice paddies ever since.

THE WALKING FISH

Many years ago a species of small fish lived in a stream in Vietnam. Except for their size, which was about seven or eight inches in length, they were just like all other fish. They stayed in the little stream where they were protected from the big fish which might eat them.

The little fish worked and played and were quite happy. The mothers watched over the eggs in the sandy bottom so the frogs and snakes wouldn't steal them. The father fish gathered food and guarded the entrance to the stream where it ran into the river. The children all went to school. Each night the fish all got together and sang songs and danced. Then before they went home there were prayers of thanks for their wonderful life.

In school the boys and girls learned many things. The boys were taught how to find food and the girls learned to guard the eggs and how to chase off intruders. All the children were warned about the river. The teacher would say, "Children, you must never go into the river. The big fish which live there would try to catch you and eat you." Then the teacher would describe the big fish, and draw a picture of them. And she would continue, "The water in the river is not like our water. It is very dirty and flows very swiftly. We would have difficulty swimming in it. But the biggest danger is the flood gates. The river water is used to flood the rice fields and if you were swept through a gate into a field you could not escape."

The children had been hearing these same things in school for years and years. And they had all learned their lessons well because no one had ever gone into the river. The fish had lived happily in their little stream without misfortune or trouble. But the trouble-free days ended when Chad was born.

Chad was a happy-go-lucky, care-free boy. He loved adventure. He was also a trouble maker. Chad would skip school and go for long swims way up the stream. When he did go to school he would ask silly questions and make smart remarks. He would disrupt the whole class. Oh, of course Chad was punished for his naughtiness. The teacher kept him after school and on holidays he was not allowed to play with the other children. But Chad just would not behave.

In spite of his wrong-doings Chad had many friends. Several of the other children thought of him as being clever and looked up to him. Chad started a club, and of course all the members chose him as the leader. The whole club would skip school and go on long swims. At night while all the other fish were having fun at their nightly get-togethers Chad and his club would hold meetings. One night at a meeting Chad told them he had made a decision. He said, "Friends, I do not believe all these stories the teacher tells us about the river. Surely it can not be as bad as she says. I think the old ones are afraid that if we find out how nice it is out there we will all leave this lonely little stream. I for one am going to find out about it and all who want to can come with me." He went on further to say that as soon as the singing started the guards would be listening to the songs, and they could easily slip by unnoticed. The whole group wanted to go and at the right moment they slipped away.

It had been very easy getting by the guards and once they were in the river they turned and swam down stream. Of course the current was so swift they had no other

choice. At first it was fun, being carried along so fast, but they had difficulty trying to stop. It was pretty muddy too and hard to see each other. Then tragedy struck. Some of the smaller ones had gotten out too far and before they could get back to the bank a big fish caught, and ate, five of them. So far the things the teacher had said were true.

Chad found a hiding place along the bank out of the swift current and he called to the rest of them. The rest of the little fish came to Chad and when the last one was there a roll call was taken. There were eleven fish missing. Chad, still acting like a fearless leader, said it was their own fault. Then he said, "Don't worry, I'll take you back to the stream if that's what you want. We'll stay here tonight and when day comes we will be able to see all right."

How wrong Chad had been! The little fish were so tired out from their experience that they did not wake up at daylight. And the place where they were hiding was right outside a flood gate. The fish were awakened by a strange and frightening sound. While they were trying to figure out what the noise was, water began rushing through the flood gate. All at once, the fish were in a rice paddy and then the gate was closed.

Once again Chad summoned them all together and sent them out in all directions to find a way to escape. But there was no way out. When they were together again Chad admitted that he too was frightened. He said, "I have been very foolish and I am sorry. Can you forgive me?" Then, bowing down, he began to pray. Suddenly there appeared a great white fish. Chad and his friends were frightened. Then the white fish spoke: "Children of disbelief, you have been punished by being caught in this rice paddy. But you shall not die. You and all your off-spring shall live in the rice fields from this time forward. No longer will you look like other fish or live as your kindred!" So saying, the white fish was gone.

Chad and his friends had a strange feeling. When they looked at one another they saw legs where their fins had been. They soon discovered they could walk or run with ease. So they knew what the white fish meant when it had said they would not look like other fish. They would soon learn about living differently too.

As the rice grew in the field the water became shallower and shallower. When the water was nearly gone the little fish climbed to the top of the dyke and looked about until they saw another newly-flooded field. And they kept doing this until the last field had been flooded. When this one was nearly dry they buried themselves in the mud, where they stayed until the fields were again flooded for the next growing season.

Walking fish have greatly increased in number and still live in the rice paddies of Vietnam. In the evenings, when the day's work is done, you can see the farmers sitting on the dykes of newly-flooded rice fields, fishing for the little walking-fish. They make a very delicious meal.

THE SPARROW

*O*N VIETNAM there are many birds. There are birds with bright shiny feathers in a variety of colors, birds which sing gay and beautiful songs, and there are common sparrows. The little sparrow is a dull brownish color with a black throat and the only song he sings is a noisy irritating chirp.

But it wasn't always like this. A long time ago all the birds could sing and, although of different colors, they were bright and shiny, and the sparrows didn't have a black throat. Of course, the birds, like all living creatures, were put on earth for a purpose. The job the birds were given was to eat the bugs and insects which destroy crops and spread disease among people and animals.

The farmers were able to raise and harvest their crops and store the grain so everyone had enough to eat all year. There was very little sickness, and all living things were happy. The Divine Spirit provided enough food for everyone.

Each evening before going to bed, the birds would sing songs and talk about the things they had done or seen that day. The birds had a council, a governing body, which consisted of one bird from each variety. The owl, being the wisest, was considered as the head of the council. There had never been any problems or trouble among the birds, so the council had not made any big decisions or punished anyone.

One evening when the birds had all met and were chatting and gossiping, the old owl began hooting loudly for silence. When everything was quiet, the owl spoke, "Fellow birds, I have some bad news I must tell you. Today I landed in a tree near one of the grain storage sheds, because I saw a group of people standing by it. They were all talking at once and I could not understand them. I flew down to a smaller tree where two men were talking, and I listened carefully. I could not understand everything they said, but I heard enough to know what they were so excited about." At this point, the birds began whispering to one another. One said to his neighbor, "I'll bet they are going to build a new granary." Another one said, "Maybe the grain is spoiling."

Then the owl hooted for silence again and spoke once more, "If you will all be quiet and pay attention, I'll tell you what I learned." Now the birds sat very still, eager to hear the news. The owl went on, "It seems as though the grain is being used up too fast. The people believe someone is stealing it. They do not think it is any of the people and no animals have been seen in town. So the people believe we birds are taking it." Now there were a great deal of *ooohs* and *aaahs;* the birds could not believe what they heard. Surely none of them could be guilty; they all had plenty of food and the ones who ate any kind of grain could get all the weed seeds they needed. Surely, the people must be mistaken.

The owl went on, "If any of you are guilty, please say so. This is very serious,

55

the people are threatening to destroy the birds." None of the birds said anything; they were all very frightened. So the owl said, "As it is late and we are all tired, the council will meet in the morning to talk this thing over and decide what is to be done." So the next morning, after a restless night, each council member flew off to the meeting place. When they were all assembled, the owl hooted for order and began speaking, "We have always lived peacefully with the people and the animals, because we have not violated any of the laws set down for us. Now there is danger of much trouble for us. Of course, there is no proof that any of us are guilty, but there is evidence that someone among us could be." The owl hesitated for a moment and then spoke again, "Since all our members have professed innocence to the charges made by the people, it is up to us to convince the people we are not guilty."

Although the birds remained silent, they began looking at one another with wondering eyes. It was as though each of them

suddenly suspected his neighbor as a law-breaker. Sensing this feeling of unrest, the owl quickly started the meeting again. He asked, "Do any of you have an idea or suggestion as to how we can solve this mystery?" The crow, raising his wing to be recognized, was given the floor. The crow said, "I say we place guards near all the granaries until we catch the culprit." A little red-bird seconded the motion and the birds all voted to try the crow's plan. So each council member was assigned to a guard post. As there were so many birds, each one would have to stay on duty only two hours at a time.

The meeting was adjourned, and each bird who had the first two-hour watch, flew to his assigned place. When they were relieved, they reported to the owl, and told him everything they had seen. At the end of a week no unusual incidents had been reported.

The grain was still being taken. It wasn't going quite as fast now, but still it was disappearing. So the owl, without saying anything to the other birds, flew around from post to post and watched the watchers. At the second place the owl visited the sparrow was on duty. As the owl sat watching, hidden by the leaves, a group of sparrows flew in and one at a time they went into the granary, took a big beak full of rice and flew off. Just before the sparrow was to go off duty, all his friends left, and he was alone. When the bluebird came to take over, the sparrow said, "I think this is a waste of time and foolish. None of us has seen anything suspicious, and I, for one, think we should stop this nonsense!" The bluebird answered, "Perhaps you are right, brother sparrow. Why don't you find the owl and ask for a council meeting tomorrow?"

The next morning, when the council was assembled, the owl said, "We have been watching the grain sheds and have learned nothing, so we will stop. I will go to the top of the hill and speak to our Divine One. I will ask for the power to speak to the leader of the people. I will tell him what we have done and learned. I will ask him not to harm any of us." So the owl flew off to the hill top, and the rest of the birds went back to their friends.

When the owl arrived in the village, he went to the home of the ruler. Although he hadn't told the other birds, he knew the guilty party, and he had a plan. The town ruler was surprised when the owl spoke to him but was pleased when he heard the news. The owl revealed his plan to the ruler by saying, "I dare not accuse the sparrows without proof. So I have obtained some magic powder from the Divine One which I shall spread on the grain. When the sparrows come to steal the grain, the magic powder will get on their feathers and will mark them as the thieves. This evening, when all the birds are gathered, I will tell them what I have told you and say the magic words which will make a black mark on the throat of the guilty sparrows. In this way all people will know which bird is guilty and will destroy only the sparrow."

That evening, when the birds were gathered for their nightly singing, the owl once again hooted for silence. He told the birds what had happened that day. Then he said the magic words, "Toi gio bat dau," which means, "It is time to begin." When he finished, each male sparrow had a large black blotch on his throat, and all the sparrows lost their brilliant color and became a dull brown. Then the owl spoke, "You have disgraced us and have lied to us. You will be known to man as thieves and grain stealers. No longer will you sing a beautiful song, and your black throat shall be a warning to all creatures to obey the laws of their gods and the rules of honest living."

The frightened sparrows flew off in all directions and have stayed to themselves ever since. The common house sparrow or English sparrow now lives in every part of the world. Only the males have a black throat, because they were the original thieves. They are stealing yet! So each time we see a sparrow with his black throat, let us remember not to lie or steal as he did. And let us remember that the liars and the thieves are always caught!